Made in the USA
Coppell, TX
23 February 2023

13295214R00070